THE STORY OF
CIVILIZATION

VOLUME IV
THE HISTORY OF THE UNITED STATES

Activity Book

TAN

Authored by Jennifer Klucinec

Illustrations by Chris Pelicano, Caroline Green

ISBN: 978-1-5051-1151-4

Printed and bound in the United States of America

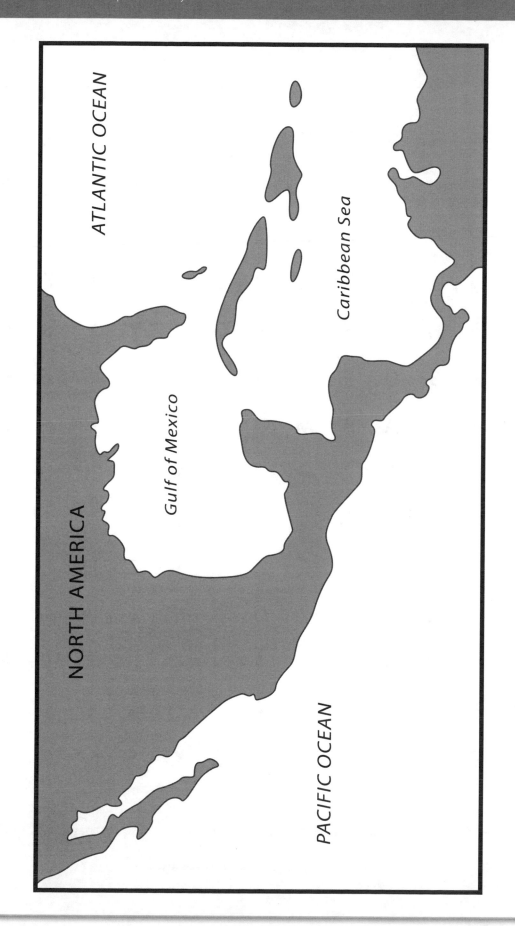

```
P A P Y I F A E A Z M V H A D
T A B K S F R E S F C R H T C
V I G U F C V W M C S R W P L
Y V W A C P D Q Q C N T I F K
P E O A N Z E U Q S A L E V D
S B Z H A S U Y Q I Y E S B I
Z C R S O P I U N Y M W Z H E
Z Z A I A A M O V R S R P L G
S C E N O Z P C O V P R Q N O
Z H O A O O V Z F S N X I N B
U I V P G T E X E A Z D O V U
K B U S W T O Q B T I D E X S
U Z N V R W X T P O B E F K P
N N V O T N S Y J Q K V D K E
M M C S M A Z T E C S M G L O
```

Find the words: Spanish, Cortez, Cuba, Aztecs, Diego, Totonacs, Velasquez, pagans, Taino, serfs

Note: Some words may appear backwards.

Read the section entitled "Escape from Tenochtitlan" to answer the following question.

The Spaniards had to escape the Aztec capital with many losses. After he was safe, Cortez sat beside a tree and cried for all the dead. The Spaniards would remember this night as what?

Once you have written in the correct answer, you should have a numeric symbol for some of the letters. Fill in a numeric symbol for the remaining letters of your own choosing (make sure to not repeat a number already used) to complete your code, then write out a short message to your sibling or mom or dad (you may want to use a scrap sheet of paper to practice your coded message). Give it to them to decipher.

A	B	C	D	E	F	G	H	I	J	K	L	M	N	O	P	Q	R	S	T	U	V	W	X	Y	Z
				5																					

$$\frac{}{20}\ \frac{}{26} \qquad \frac{}{16}\ \frac{}{11}\ \frac{}{24}\ \frac{}{15}\ \frac{E}{5} \qquad \frac{}{18}\ \frac{}{12}\ \frac{}{6}\ \frac{}{23}\ \frac{}{18}\ \frac{E}{5}$$

Across

2. Coronado sought a water passage to _____.
5. State where De Soto died
8. Explored the coast of Florida
9. First to see Colorado River

Down

1. State where Fr. Segura and companions were martyred
3. State where Fr. Padilla said mass of Thanksgiving
4. _____ de Soto was the first European to cross Mississippi River
6. City of first college in North America
7. Founded St. Augustine

Champlain died in 1637 but is still remembered by what title?

NAEVOZRRZA

RACETRI

LUGF FO TS. AWLREENC

QUISIROO

TYERUAS

LIAMCHPAN

WEN FRCAEN

BEUQEC

RFU DEATR

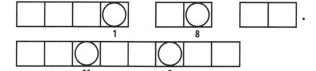
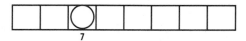
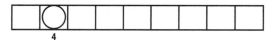
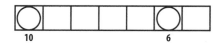

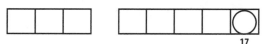

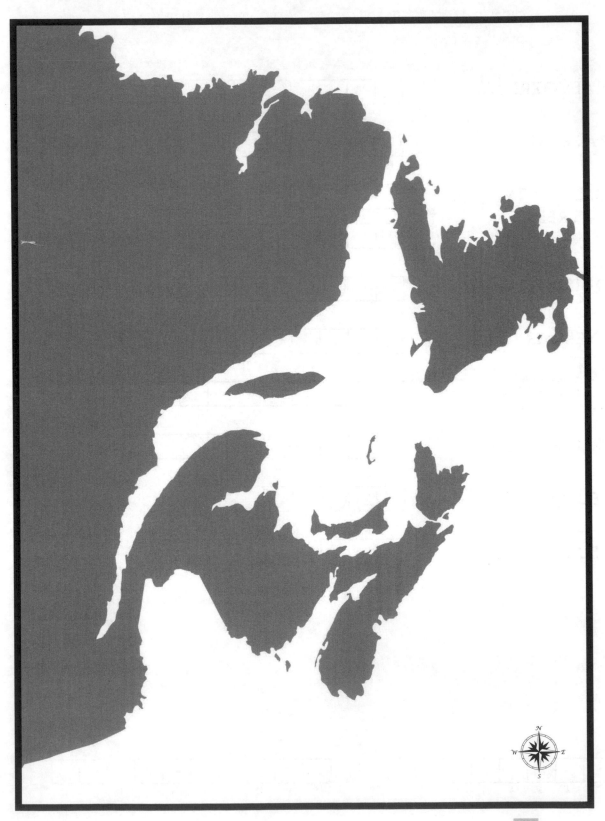

= Land

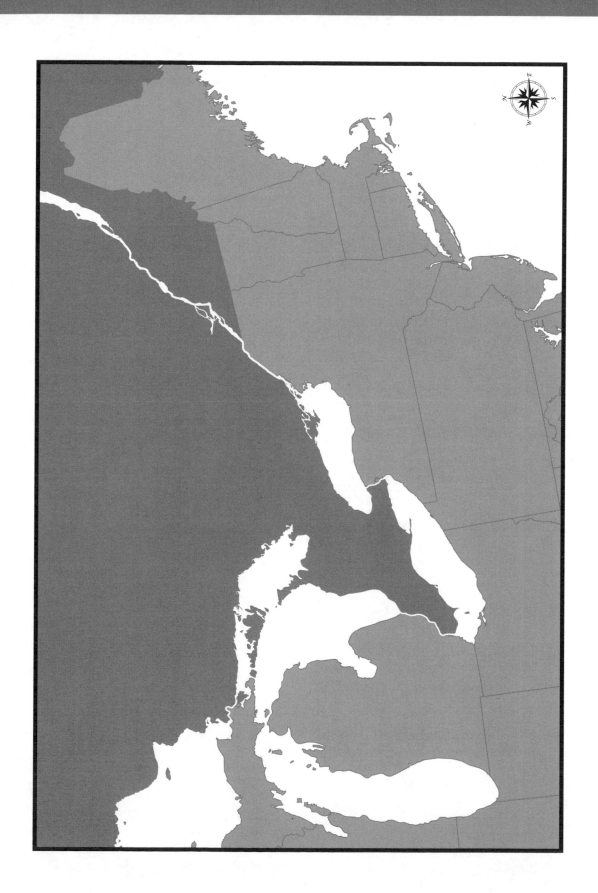

Fill in the blanks for the La Salle word search clues and then find the corresponding words in the word search.

1. La Salle purchased land near _____ and set up a trading post.

2. In 1670 he came upon the _____ River.

3. He also sailed on Lake _____.

4. La Salle came from the country of _____.

5. He was the first European to sail on the _____ Lakes.

6. His beautiful sailing vessel was called the _____.

7. His boat was built to carry _____.

8. La Salle's boat eventually sank in Lake _____.

```
W  B  E  Q  C  Z  M  G  K  U  F  Q  R  F  G
F  C  N  C  U  F  R  I  H  P  O  T  N  G  W
R  P  G  U  N  I  L  S  C  V  C  A  U  I  A
K  L  R  Z  F  A  R  M  O  H  O  E  U  Y  T
O  L  A  F  W  U  R  K  M  J  I  R  Z  X  T
N  M  O  E  F  C  C  F  Z  P  Z  G  W  W  G
T  N  P  C  C  Z  J  Y  P  J  L  G  A  Z  S
A  C  E  B  E  U  Q  I  M  V  V  K  W  N  E
R  K  Y  U  B  I  S  J  Z  R  M  L  P  N  F
I  R  Y  J  C  S  P  O  Y  K  B  R  C  D  M
O  Q  S  X  I  M  L  Y  U  W  U  V  W  U  Z
R  A  N  S  U  C  B  M  N  B  H  X  F  M  W
A  R  S  B  I  R  M  Z  O  V  P  F  Q  Q  K
F  I  U  S  M  L  U  S  S  J  T  X  D  L  O
M  L  D  A  V  N  X  Q  F  W  W  J  S  T  E
```

Note: Some words may appear backwards.

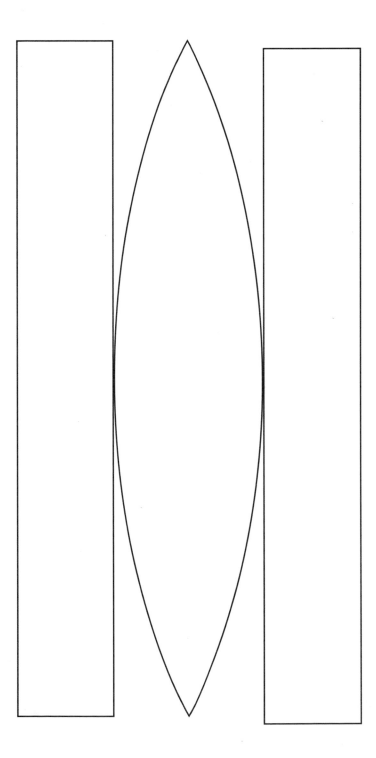

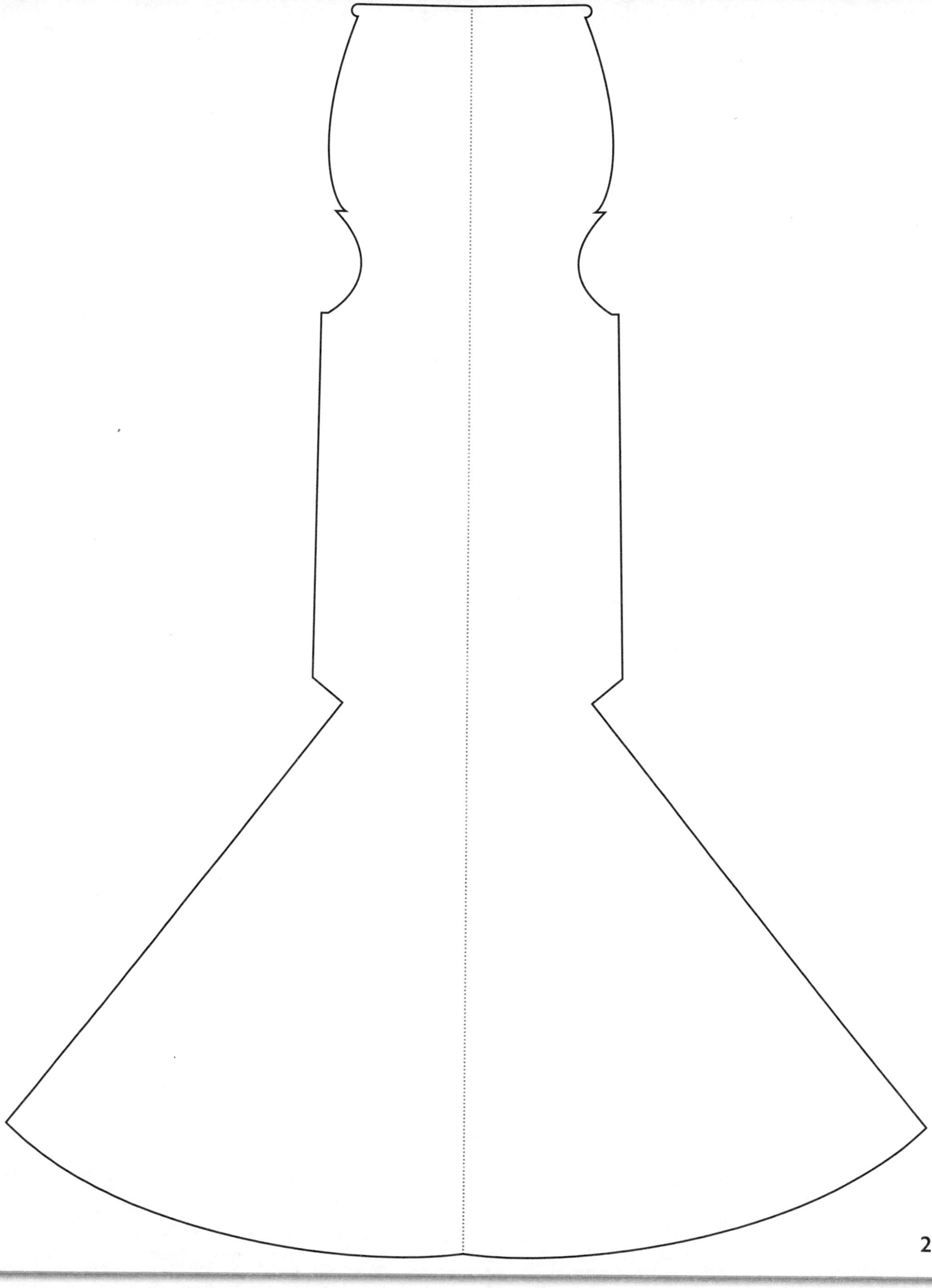

Read the section entitled "England's Early Struggles in the New World" to answer the following question.

When English ships returned to Roanoke in 1590, they found the colony abandoned. Even the houses were dismantled. The only clue left behind was this mysterious word carved into a tree?

Once you have written in the correct answer, you should have a numeric symbol for some of the letters. Fill in a numeric symbol for the remaining letters of your own choosing (make sure to not repeat a number already used) to complete your code, then write out a short message to your sibling or mom or dad (you may want to use a scrap sheet of paper to practice your coded message). Give it to them to decipher.

A	B	C	D	E	F	G	H	I	J	K	L	M	N	O	P	Q	R	S	T	U	V	W	X	Y	Z
														3											

```
__  __  O  __  __  O  __  __
13  26  3  16   1  3  16   4
```

Across

3. _____ especially loved smoking Virginia tobacco.

7. Rolfe had been to the English colony in _____.

8. John _____ solved the problem of Jamestown not making any money.

9. The local tribes did not like tobacco farming because it took up too much _____.

10. Violent clashes began between the _____ and the English

1. Jamestown colony was not making any _____ for the Virginia Company.

2. Rolfe brought back some seeds from the _____.

4. By the 1620's the _____ of Jamestown was secured.

5. Jamestown was making money for the Virginia Company through the _____ of tobacco.

6. _____ grew very well in the climate.

CHARACTERS: PILGRIM 1, PILGRIM 2, INDIAN 1, INDIAN 2

SETTING: Outside a pilgrim's house near the garden.

PILGRIM 1: Wow! Look at all these crops!
PILGRIM 2: I know! We have a lot to be thankful for. This autumn has been generous to us.
PILGRIM 1: And it's a good thing we made friends with the Wampanoag tribe and its chief.
PILGRIM 2: You can say that again!
PILGRIM 1: It's a good thing we made friends with——
PILGRIM 2: I didn't mean it literally!
PILGRIM 1: Oh.

Indian 1 and Indian 2 enter the garden.

INDIAN 1: Me heard the word "thankful."
INDIAN 2: Ya, me heard it too. We Wampanoag thankful to make peace with you Puritans.
INDIAN 1: You say that again!
INDIAN 2: We Wampanoag thankful to make peace with——
PILGRIM 1: He didn't really mean literally. I would know (says sarcastically and glancing at Pilgrim 2).
INDIAN 1: I have idea. We have lots of corn and turkeys to eat.
PILGRIM 2: And we have lots of vegetable and fruits that are ready to be picked and eaten.
INDIAN 2: We all share this together. Make one big feast.
PILGRIM 1: Why don't you call your people and I'll call mine.
PILGRIM 2: Ya, we'll make it a big celebration with the Puritans and the Wampanoags.
INDIAN 1: We do that. Be right back.
INDIAN 2: Yes, be right back.

Indians exit stage and return with various food items and place them on a table.

Pilgrims bring their food items to the table.

PILGRIM 1: Now let us say a prayer of Thanksgiving before we eat.

All bow heads.

PILGRIM 2: Thank you, Heavenly Father, for this bounty we are about to receive.
ALL: Amen

All pretend to eat.

Indian 1 and Indian 2: Food good!
Pilgrim 1 and Pilgrim 2: You can say that again!
Indian 1 and Indian 2: Food good!

THE END

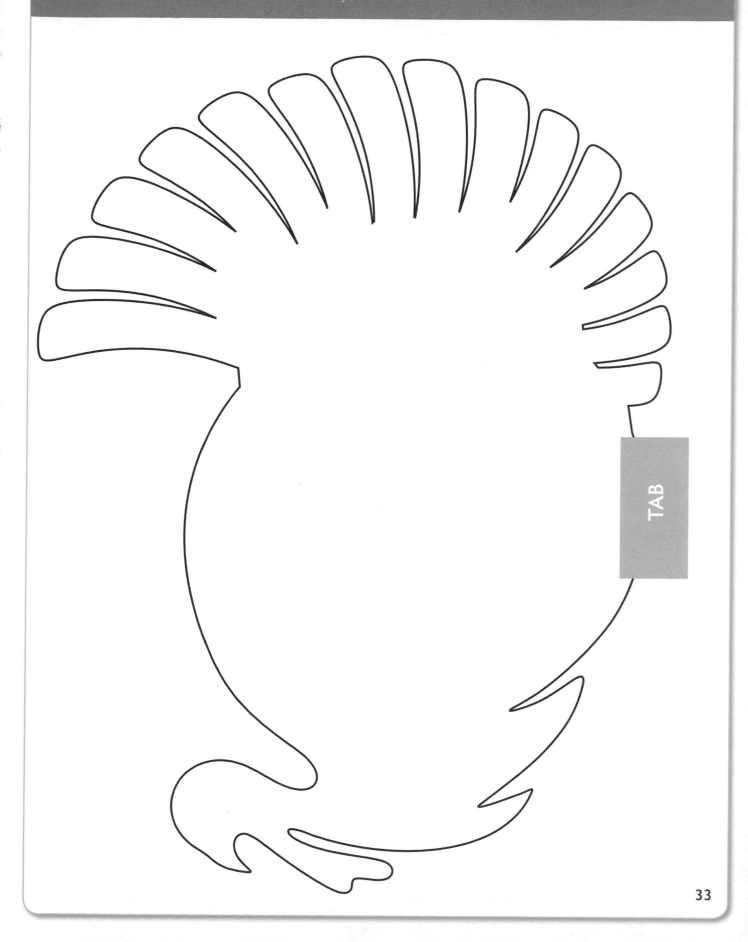

TAB

What was a person called who signed an agreement to work for a certain number of years in exchange for transportation to the colonies?

NTERSUHO LEISOCNO

WEN DALGENN

RICNAAF

OGGEARI

HIBRIST SILCOONE

NERTASPOTT

TS. ETERP VELRAC

CANNSFIARC SARRFI

1	2	3	4	5	6	7	8	9	3

10	11	12	13	14	15	16	17

```
E  W  Q  Y  N  D  W  P  L  E  C  Q  A  S  D
N  C  O  L  O  N  I  E  S  S  Z  X  N  H  F
H  U  S  T  N  A  V  R  E  S  M  A  D  N  B
M  R  I  S  T  L  L  S  Q  J  T  G  R  P  B
C  J  O  P  F  Y  C  E  L  I  Z  P  O  A  K
X  I  U  C  T  R  O  C  R  A  T  M  L  V  A
C  H  L  Y  U  A  H  U  K  W  V  T  T  G  M
Q  G  Q  O  Y  M  P  T  F  L  I  E  E  J  E
P  I  L  I  H  P  X  E  U  M  Z  O  R  I  R
L  S  P  L  O  T  J  D  O  O  R  Z  M  Y  I
X  G  S  M  P  G  A  R  D  G  S  H  J  I  C
D  C  O  C  N  E  E  C  I  K  Y  N  I  M  A
B  G  Z  I  H  R  M  A  O  F  H  V  C  Y  G
R  S  K  Y  W  H  N  T  Y  S  P  Y  K  L  J
B  G  S  E  U  V  X  D  Q  G  A  E  Q  A  R
```

Find the words: servants, Catholic, slavery, South America, Georgia, Maryland, Lord Baltimore, Puritans, persecuted, colonies, King Philip

Note: Some words may appear backwards.

Help the Catholics escape persecution to Maryland

Start

MARYLAND

After reading Chapter 8, answer the following question.

With the loss of Quebec, the French could no longer maintain the war effort in North America. The French and Indian War officially ended in 1763 with what?

Once you have written in the correct answer, you should have a numeric symbol for most of the letters. Fill in a numeric symbol for the remaining letters of your own choosing (make sure to not repeat a number already used) to complete your code, then write out a short message to your sibling or mom or dad (you may want to use a scrap sheet of paper to practice your coded message). Give it to them to decipher.

A	B	C	D	E	F	G	H	I	J	K	L	M	N	O	P	Q	R	S	T	U	V	W	X	Y	Z
					24																				

     __ __ __   __ __ __   __ __   __ __ __ __   F __ __ __ __ __ __ __ __

     10 4 22   22 6 25   11 24   7 11 11 17   24 22 22 26 21 20 7 2

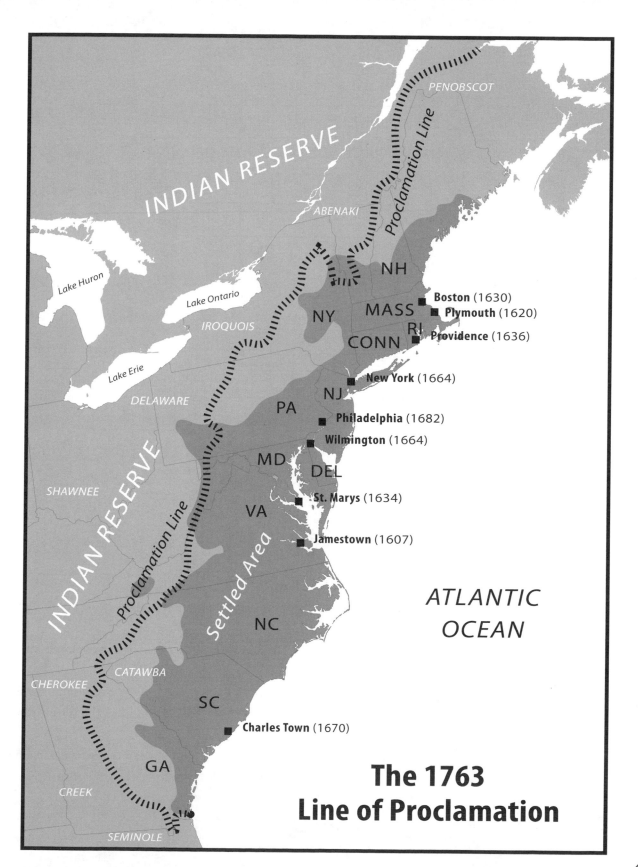

INDIAN RESERVE

Proclamation Line

PENOBSCOT

ABENAKI

Lake Huron

Lake Ontario

IROQUOIS

Lake Erie

DELAWARE

SHAWNEE

INDIAN RESERVE

Proclamation Line

NH

NY

MASS

CONN

RI

Boston (1630)

Plymouth (1620)

Providence (1636)

New York (1664)

NJ

PA

Philadelphia (1682)

Wilmington (1664)

MD

DEL

St. Marys (1634)

VA

Settled Area

Jamestown (1607)

NC

CATAWBA

CHEROKEE

SC

Charles Town (1670)

GA

CREEK

SEMINOLE

ATLANTIC OCEAN

The 1763 Line of Proclamation

Across

3. The king and _____ hoped to create a homeland for North American native tribes.

5. The colonists resented the _____ of 1763.

6. The violent event in March of 1770 was known as the _____ Massacre.

8. The number of colonies was _____.

Down

1. The colonists were told they could not settle west of the _____ Mountains.

2. Britain won control of Louisiana, all the way to the _____ River Valley.

4. In 1773 the Sons of Liberty disguised themselves as _____ as they dumped the tea into the harbor.

7. King _____ and Parliament were determined to punish Boston for this act.

Many colonists argued that the Stamp Act was illegal and that Parliament could not tax them directly because it was passed without their consent and they didn't have any representation in Parliament. This phrase summed up their argument: _____.

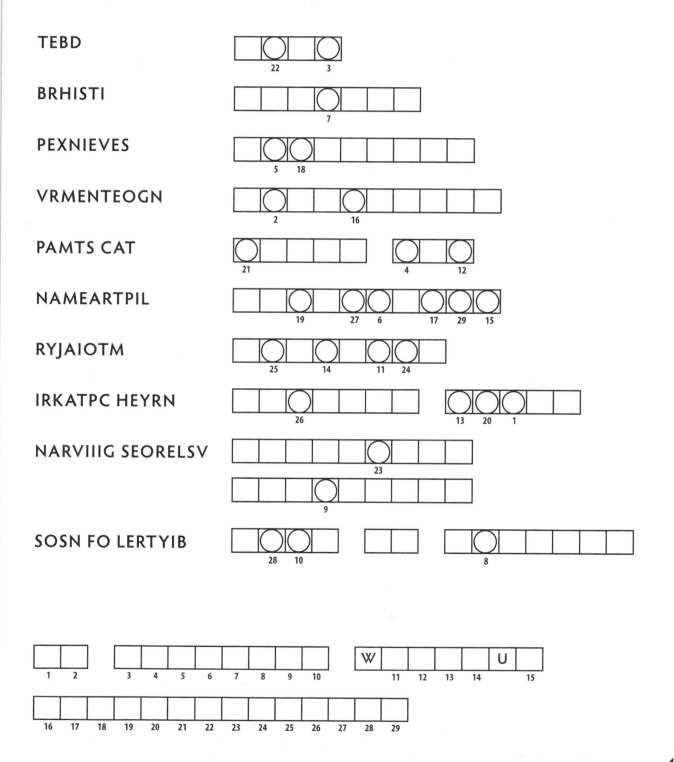

TEBD

BRHISTI

PEXNIEVES

VRMENTEOGN

PAMTS CAT

NAMEARTPIL

RYJAIOTM

IRKATPC HEYRN

NARVIIIG SEORELSV

SOSN FO LERTYIB

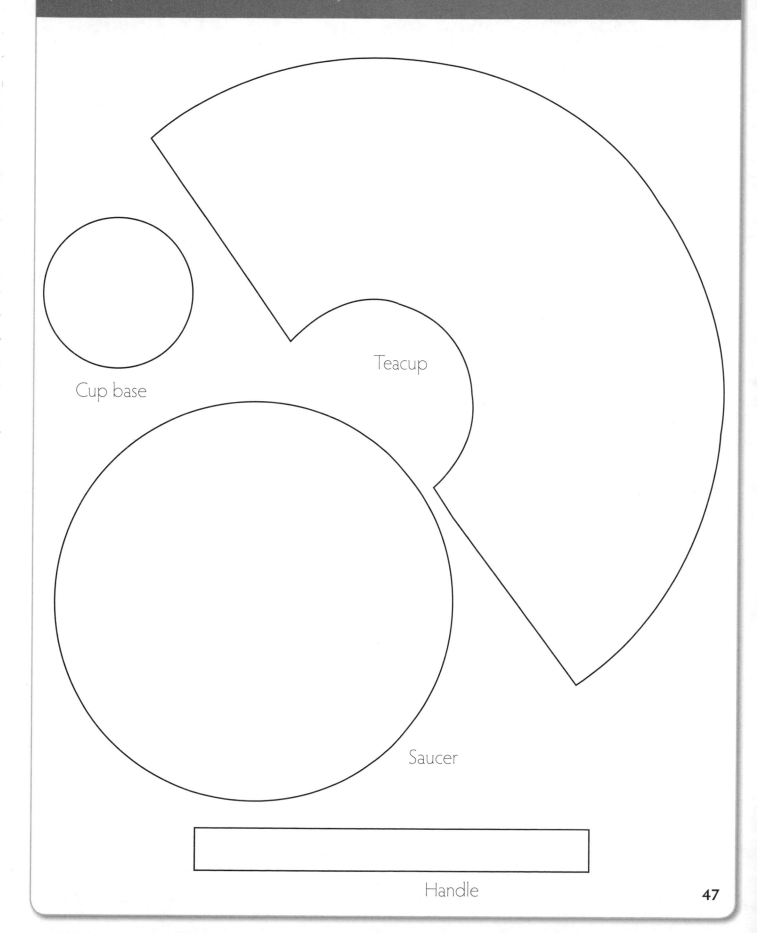

Cup base

Teacup

Saucer

Handle

A P A C T R T L H E I S S E L F A J S

E O R I H S V G S G O O Q J N V J S P

B O S T O N H A R B O R N I W C E A C

N Q D F M T P K G L F W H K O R U P C

X N G X A A A W Q M Z C V J G L B S S

F O E Q S R R G M V P I T N R P Y X Q

L T B G P N Y I M Q X T O E M B R R J

I G S Y A G S T Z S A C V X Q U H D X

O N V H I C P K T Q L E C O N C O R D

G I D R N F S O E A R U Z B T Z V L E

P H W E E A I A T E G R O E G G N I K

N S G Y P R U N M M C O X O O D N X L

B A E Y T E E J L O A U C O T M R I H

P W G A Z N N J H N H G N I I L G K L

D N P B I Q T D K E Z T U E L O X I Q

F O D T G M R J E J E R D V X F Q N

W L N O Y G N B V N U R K J P H C F O

Y O L K K K N W H M C H S K F Z J K H

C S O C W K M M K Y Q E C Y O J K N K

Find the words: Patriots, Paul Revere, Boston Harbor, King George, Thomas Cage, Continental Congress, Washington, Concord, Independence, Thomas Paine

Note: Some words may appear backwards.

Which document turned the United States into a confederacy and was the first attempt of establishing a government?

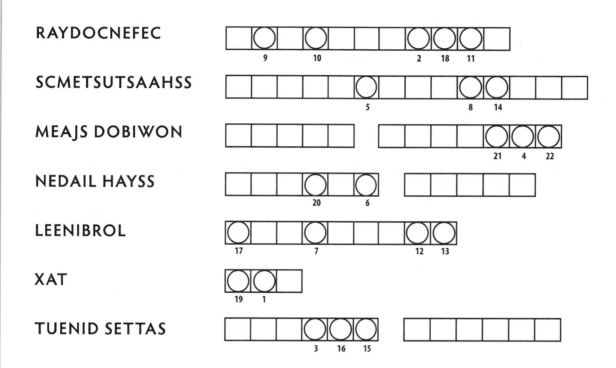

RAYDOCNEFEC

SCMETSUTSAAHSS

MEAJS DOBIWON

NEDAIL HAYSS

LEENIBROL

XAT

TUENID SETTAS

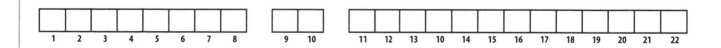

After reading Chapter 11, answer the following question.

The Convention of 1787 decided that the new government should have these three different parts. Read the section "The Blueprint of a Republic" to help find the answers.

Once you have written in the correct answer, you should have a numeric symbol for most of the letters. Fill in a numeric symbol for the remaining letters of your own choosing (make sure to not repeat a number already used) to complete your code, then write out a short message to your sibling or mom or dad (you may want to use a scrap sheet of paper to practice your coded message). Give it to them to decipher.

A	B	C	D	E	F	G	H	I	J	K	L	M	N	O	P	Q	R	S	T	U	V	W	X	Y	Z
				5																					

    <u> </u> <u>E</u> <u> </u> <u> </u> <u> </u> <u> </u> <u> </u> <u> </u> <u> </u> <u> </u> <u>E</u> , <u> </u> <u>E</u> <u> </u> <u>E</u> <u> </u> <u> </u> <u> </u> <u> </u> <u>E</u> ,

    22 5 13 7 3 22 14 4 7 18 5   5 20 5 2 16 4 7 18 5

                  <u> </u> <u> </u> <u> </u> <u> </u> <u> </u> <u> </u> <u> </u> <u> </u>

                  21 16 12 7 2 7 14 22

Across

2. Did not like Hamilton's ideas
5. Means example or pattern
7. Another name for the 10 Amendments
10. The second president

Down

1. Washington's home
3. Wanted the federal government to be strong
4. Temporary capital of the U.S.
6. The first president
8. The Secretary of the Treasury
9. Was an anti-federalist

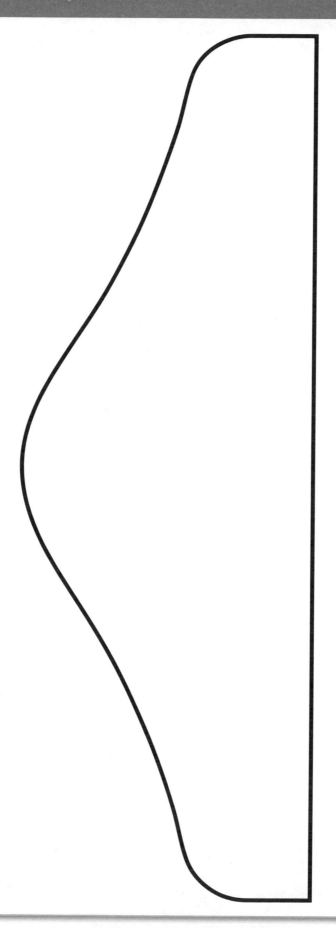

1

2

3

4

5

6

7

8

9

10

Protection from Unreasonable Searches and Seizures

Rights of Accused Persons in Criminal Cases

The Right to Bear Arms

Undelegated Powers Kept by the States and the People

Other Rights not mentioned in the Constitution

Right to due process of law, no double jeopardy or self-incrimination

Right to trial by jury in Civil Cases

Freedom of Religion, Speech, and the Press

The Housing of Soldiers

Excessive Bail, Fines, and Punishments Forbidden

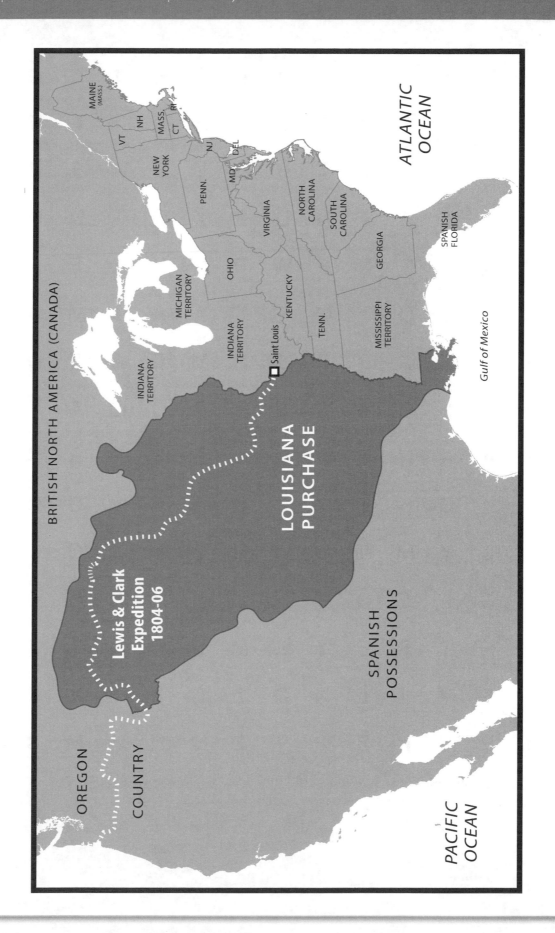

```
C  C  O  W  I  J  A  V  P  G  R  J  C  G  M
S  T  F  H  I  M  J  D  G  H  Q  I  F  K  A
V  A  D  T  E  E  T  B  O  Y  B  W  S  P  X
B  R  I  T  A  I  N  D  P  X  Q  T  N  N  T
D  N  A  L  G  N  E  W  E  N  N  X  E  E  O
A  S  X  Z  O  I  O  F  X  A  A  I  M  D  D
Q  J  T  S  S  R  R  S  H  M  C  A  B  D  V
Q  R  M  L  Z  A  S  C  R  P  Q  M  A  I  W
W  N  A  A  N  T  R  U  I  E  B  P  R  B  T
A  N  K  C  H  E  M  K  P  A  F  V  G  R  E
D  J  E  Y  M  M  D  W  H  G  B  F  O  O  W
I  I  G  E  C  D  S  N  Y  Y  M  Q  E  F  L
G  H  H  T  B  E  Y  W  M  U  Q  N  T  J  P
S  A  F  M  J  L  X  O  Z  G  Z  I  Y  R  T
X  T  B  V  R  B  R  J  Z  M  N  W  M  B  U
```

Find the words: Jefferson, Britain, Forbidden, Merchants, Sailors, Rhode Island, New England, Embargo, France

Note: Some words may appear backwards.

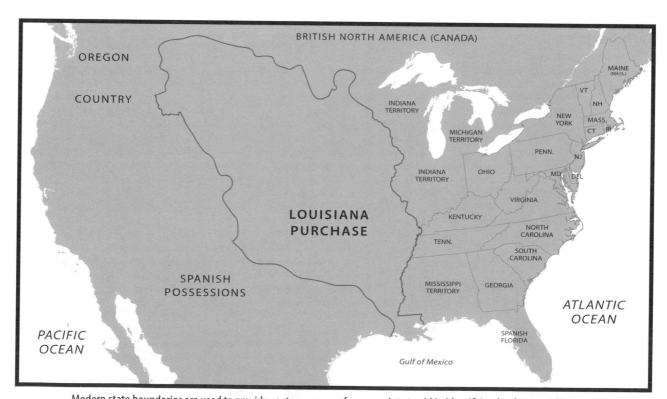

Modern state boundaries are used to provide contemporary reference points to aid in identifying landmass and location.

THE LOUISIANA PURCHASE

$15,000,000

800,000 SQUARE MILES OF LAND

The last battle of the War of 1812 was _____

SECNAMAIR
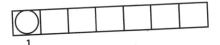
10

TISRIBH
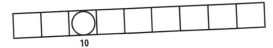
1

DAACNA
2   16

TAYTER FO HETGN
4   7 8

DENWAR NAJCSOK
13 6 11   18 12

CUKTENYK
15 17

NALOISAIU
5

VUTRNSEELO
14   3

RIESUNLU
9

1 2 3 4 5 6   7 8   9 10 11   12 13 10 14 15 16 17 18

8

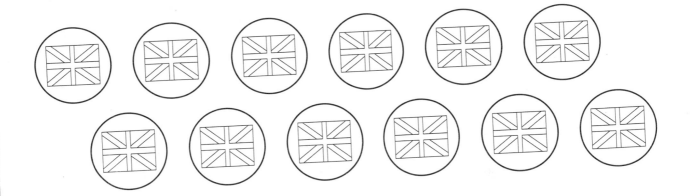

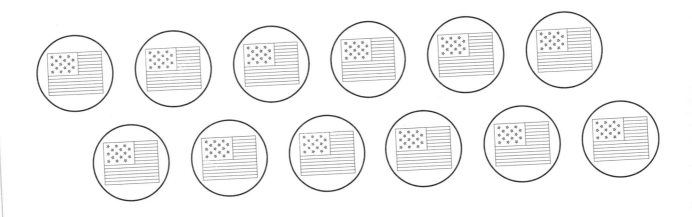

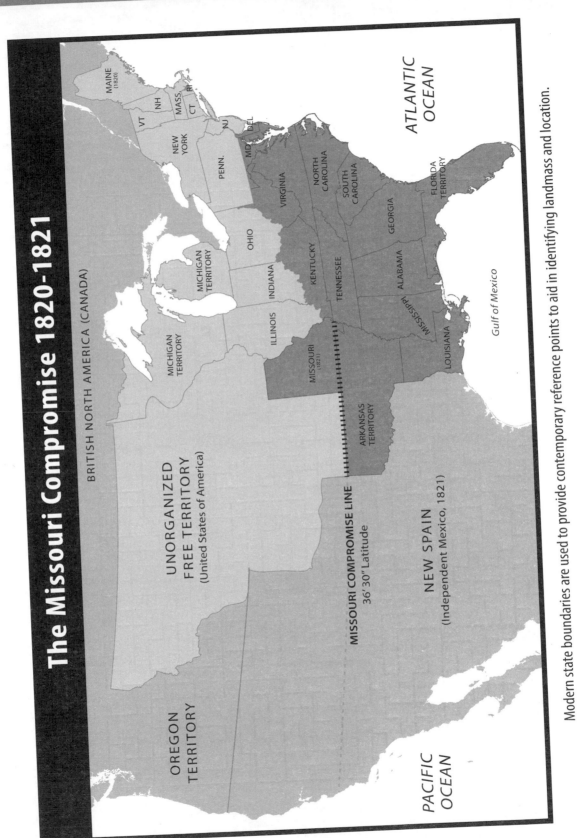

The Missouri Compromise 1820-1821

Map: The Missouri Compromise 1820-1821

BRITISH NORTH AMERICA (CANADA)

ATLANTIC OCEAN

MAINE (1820)

VT

NH

MASS.

CT

RI

NEW YORK

NJ

PENN.

DEL

MD

VIRGINIA

NORTH CAROLINA

SOUTH CAROLINA

GEORGIA

FLORIDA TERRITORY

OHIO

MICHIGAN TERRITORY

INDIANA

ILLINOIS

KENTUCKY

TENNESSEE

ALABAMA

MISSISSIPPI

MICHIGAN TERRITORY

MISSOURI (1821)

ARKANSAS TERRITORY

LOUISIANA

Gulf of Mexico

UNORGANIZED FREE TERRITORY
(United States of America)

MISSOURI COMPROMISE LINE
36'30' Latitude

NEW SPAIN
(Independent Mexico, 1821)

OREGON TERRITORY

PACIFIC OCEAN

Modern state boundaries are used to provide contemporary reference points to aid in identifying landmass and location.

Across

4. Was chosen as president even though he didn't win popular vote
6. Number of senators each state has
7. Won the popular vote of the election of 1824.

Down

1. The supporters of Jackson became known as the _____ Party.
2. Neither Jackson nor Adams had enough of these to win.
3. The supporters of Adams became known as the _____ Party.
5. Jackson and his _____ were outraged.

After reading chapter 15, answer the following question.

After years of arguments between the Federalists and the Democratic Republicans, it was nice to have a time without political strife. Americans felt optimistic about the future and wanted to come together to improve their country. Due to the general feeling of optimism, this time has been called _____.

Once you have written in the correct answer, you should have a numeric symbol for most of the letters. Fill in a numeric symbol for the remaining letters of your own choosing (make sure to not repeat a number already used) to complete your code, then write out a short message to your sibling or mom or dad (you may want to use a scrap sheet of paper to practice your coded message). Give it to them to decipher.

A	B	C	D	E	F	G	H	I	J	K	L	M	N	O	P	Q	R	S	T	U	V	W	X	Y	Z
					24																				

___ ___ ___   ___ ___ ___   ___ ___   ___ ___ ___ ___   F ___ ___ ___ ___ ___ ___ ___
10 4 22   22 6 25   11 24   7 11 11 17   24 22 22 26 21 20 7 2

```
Y O T J R L S F R G G E T D P H
H T N X H A R L K F N W E A U T
M I I V P F I P A I C Y X O Z D
F S N R C S D L G N N V T R U X
B S E X A A K N R E A V I L N Z
X O C E N H E L W O M C L A O A
Y K H U M C C O M A R E N T V
T T K D A U O F E B R D S O E T
O G O E Z M K H O O S G S I S Y
J M T U E B B N R S V Y L T H A
O S G N A N Y M P J R B Q A S M
J O H N C A R R O L L E S N A W
H L N R G V Y A O Z J Y T H M Z
I W B W D I D H V L I F Y S T A
X Z Q N X P G K G Z E U X L I K
K P K W S E G R A B G M L W G S
```

Note: Some words may appear backwards.

Find the words: Textiles, Newcomen, Steam engine, Railroads, National Road, Barges, Canals, Seton, John Carroll, Sisters of Charity

In 1830, President Andrew Jackson signed a law known as the_____.

KSCOJNA

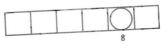

NIVTEA MERNIASAC

 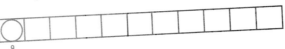

SERBIT

RYAM

KEHCEROE

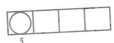

LIART OF RTEAS

 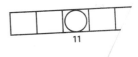

SRTIHG

PIIPIISSSMS VERRI

 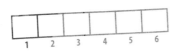

SETESIDR

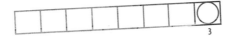 

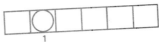

Across

1. A state added after Jackson left office.
3. Jackson had a deep mistrust in these people.
6. Sad event for the Cherokees
9. Refuse to enforce

Down

2. Money U.S. government has borrowed is called the _____ debt.
4. Jackson's nickname was Old _____.
5. Jackson's vice president
7. Tax paid on goods
8. Patronage is also called the Spoils _____.

```
K F K O M A L A Z Z H A B R F
T T E K C O R C O J H W O R E
U S A T R N S S O R K H W X T
W W N H I Q T A N E I N I R I
V R C T C P M N M O S O E M Z
W D S Q L X U P L A T I D U L
V U Y K T P N A N S U S N R V
A M B E Y V D T G A R S U R V
A T X T I H A R K O G I S O Z
L A A Y Q A H I O O C M F E H
S W D Y N S E C M E X I C O S
J Y V N L V X I R V U O Q N B
A R A L P O T O N B O S H V D
P B K V E P R S H Y X O J F W
R D T Y N V J C C B Y D F K A
```

Find the words: Bowie, Austin, Crockett, Houston, Texas, Mexico, Santa Anna, Alamo, San Patricios, Taylor, Mission,

Note: Some words may appear backwards.

FINISH

GOLD
MINE　　　20 pts

GOLD NUGGET 5pts
GOLD DUST 2pts
GOLD BAR 8pts
GOLD DUST 2pts
GOLD NUGGET 5pts
GOLD DUST 2pts
GOLD NUGGET 5pts
GOLD DUST 2pts
GOLD BAR 8pts
GOLD DUST 2pts
GOLD DUST 2pts
GOLD NUGGET 5pts
GOLD DUST 2pts

GOLD NUGGET 5pts
GOLD DUST 2pts
GOLD BAR 8pts
GOLD DUST 2pts
GOLD NUGGET 5pts
GOLD DUST 2pts
GOLD DUST 2pts
GOLD DUST 2pts
GOLD NUGGET 5pts
GOLD BAR 8pts
GOLD DUST 2pts
START

Across

3. Big event of 1849
4. Perilous party
7. 1840's destination of many settlers
8. Settlers had to travel west over the _____ Mountains.
9. He discovered gold in a small creek outside a sawmill.

Down

1. California became the _____-_____ state.
2. The _____ of 1850 allowed California in the Union as a free state.
5. _____ Destiny was the belief that people were destined to spread westward to settle the entire continent.
6. The gold seekers became known as the forty _____.

This controversial law meant that escaped slaves were not safe even in the North. It also meant that people who were opposed to slavery were evil. What was this law called?

YVLESRA

⬜⬜⬜◯⬜⬜
　　　10

TOLNISSIOBAIT

⬜⬜⬜◯⬜⬜⬜⬜⬜◯◯⬜
　　　　7　　　　　　　12　18

REDD TCTOS

⬜⬜◯⬜　　⬜◯⬜⬜⬜
　　3　　　　　17

RERTIAH ATBMUN

⬜◯⬜◯◯⬜　　⬜⬜⬜⬜◯⬜
　2　　9　15　　　　　　　14

LIE WYENITH

⬜◯⬜　　⬜⬜⬜◯⬜⬜
　13　　　　　　8

DUNREGODUNR DAILORRA

⬜⬜⬜◯⬜◯⬜⬜⬜⬜
5　　11　6
⬜⬜⬜⬜⬜◯⬜
　　　　　16

MEEROFD

◯⬜⬜⬜⬜⬜
4

LENUC MOT'S CAIBN

⬜⬜⬜⬜⬜　　◯⬜⬜⬜'⬜　　⬜⬜⬜⬜⬜
　　　　　　　　1

⬜⬜⬜　⬜⬜⬜⬜⬜⬜⬜⬜　⬜⬜⬜⬜⬜　⬜⬜⬜
1　2　3　　4　5　6　7　8　9　10　11　12　13　14　10　15　16　17　18

Eli Whitney	Nat Turner
Dred Scott	Frederick Douglass
Harriet Beecher Stowe	William Lloyd Garrison

Led a rebellion murdering whites and freeing slaves

Inventor of the cotton gin

Escaped Maryland slave who spoke and wrote against slavery

Sued for his freedom arguing he should be recognized as free

Newspaper editor who spread abolitionist views

Wrote
Uncle Tom's Cabin

Sojourner Truth

Harriet Tubman

David Wilmot

John Brown

Roger Taney

Escaped slavery
then worked within
Underground Railroad
to help other
slaves escape

Escaped slave who
preached against
slavery across America

Believed the use of
violence to end slavery
was justified

Proposed slavery
be prohibited in any
territories taken
from Mexico

Catholic Chief
Justice who declared
blacks had no rights in
Dred Scott case

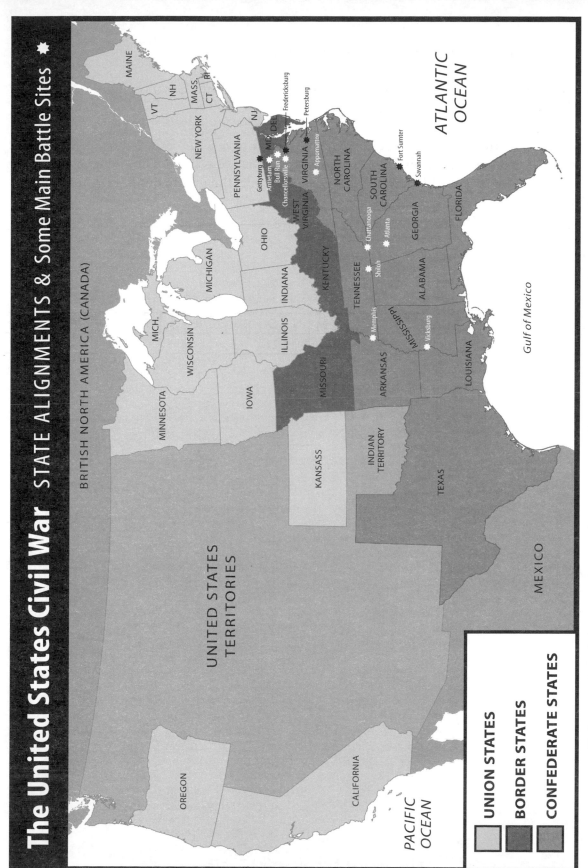

The United States Civil War   STATE ALIGNMENTS & Some Main Battle Sites ✴

UNION STATES

BORDER STATES

CONFEDERATE STATES

Modern state boundaries are used to provide contemporary reference points to aid in identifying landmass and location.

After reading chapter 21, answer the following question.

In 1861, the Confederates attacked and captured this place in South Carolina, igniting the Civil War. What was the name of this place?

Once you have written in the correct answer, you should have a numeric symbol for some of the letters. Fill in a numeric symbol for the remaining letters of your own choosing (make sure to not repeat a number already used) to complete your code, then write out a short message to your sibling or mom or dad (you may want to use a scrap sheet of paper to practice your coded message). Give it to them to decipher.

A	B	C	D	E	F	G	H	I	J	K	L	M	N	O	P	Q	R	S	T	U	V	W	X	Y	Z
														21											

```
__  O  __  __      __  __  __  __  __  __
 5  21  4   3       1  20   8   3   6   4
```

Across

2. A Confederate State
5. Another Confederate State
6. The Confederate President
9. Lincoln called for _____ after the attack at Ft. Sumter.
10. The first state to leave the Union

Down

1. _____ of the states across the south met at Secession Conventions.
3. Confederate States of _____.
4. Lincoln wanted to abolish this.
7. The Confederacy demanded Lincoln to turn over all U.S. _____.
8. Means, to leave.

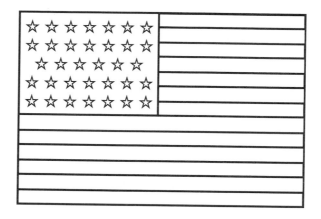

This Civil War battle resulted in the bloodiest day in US history: _____.

RENTOHRN

ENSOTRUH

REAFECDYCNO

PAMTOPTAXO

ELE

TAGRN

IVRNIGAI

LYNMARDA

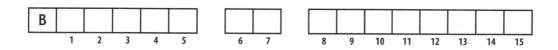

S X R Y Y R J E P S R Q X R U

J O A E W G E E T B H N E X L

Z K L E G N H N K L F C Q O Y

K X C D W G E T I J O O D T S

J G W N I M A N O N K Y O T S

I K U Y D E C B S O U R H A E

U J O N Z O R T T T B M Q M S

V K E I L E R L C E V Z Y O E

U M G N L U W G J S P J I P Y

A S E R C R J K S Q K R Z P A

N O I T U T I T S N O C A A H

H I I N O S N H O J K W Z C E

D O K Y X G V R C Q W F U E C

N D O J T L G X P U Y Y L K U

S C A L A W A G S O H Z I M K

Find the words: Reconstruction, Soldier, Ulysses, Lee, Appomattox, Lincoln, Booth, Johnson, Amendments, Constitution, Hayes, Scalawags, Carpetbagger

Note: Some words may appear backwards.

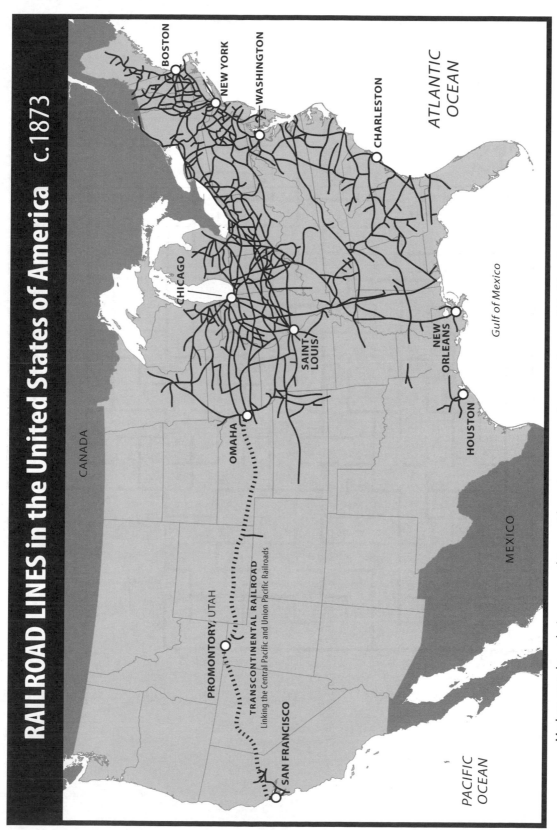

RAILROAD LINES in the United States of America c.1873

Modern state boundaries are used to provide contemporary reference points to aid in identifying landmass and location.

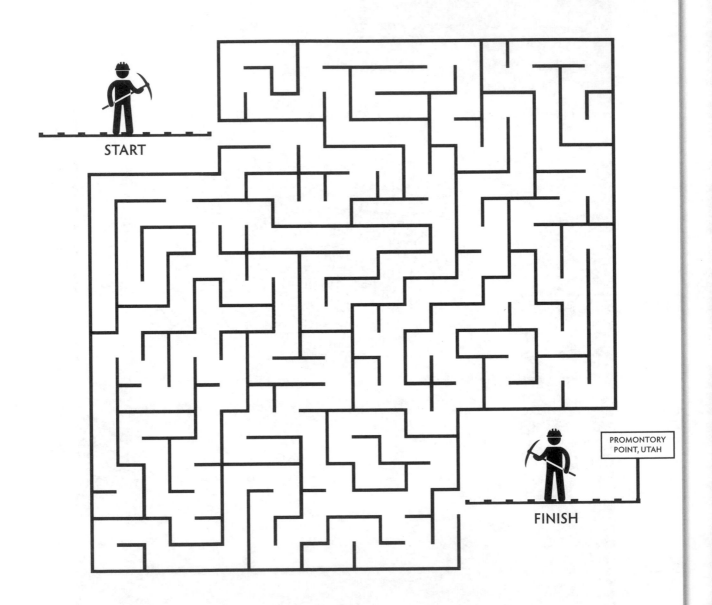

START

FINISH

PROMONTORY
POINT, UTAH

Across

4. Type of lamp oil is used for
6. Promontory _____, Utah
7. The president who helped inudstry grow in the U.S.
8. Oil Man

Down

1. Giant of the steel industry and philanthropist
2. When a company controls industry to a point where it has an unfair advantage.
3. Cleansed of all impurities
4. An alloy of iron, carbon and other elements
9. The Transcontinental _____.

In 1890, the 7th Cavalry began firing into the Sioux Village, where more than three hundred Sioux had been shot dead, including Chief Sitting Bull, also known as Crazy Horse. This event is known as _____.

TKI NASROC

ACMHENCO

GEMNIORO

ZRCYA REOHS

SIXUO

CERTUS

LAARCVY

TOSHU TAKOAD

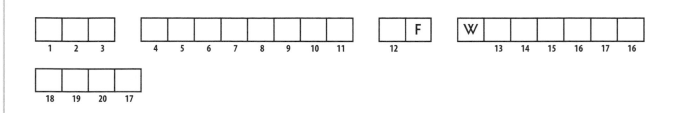

After reading chapter 25, answer the following question.

During the Spanish American War Theodore Roosevelt led a group of men consisting of college athletes, cowboys, ranchers, and minders. They stormed San Juan Hill, a key victory for the Americans. This group of men was known as _____.

Once you have written in the correct answer, you should have a numeric symbol for most of the letters. Fill in a numeric symbol for the remaining letters of your own choosing (make sure to not repeat a number already used) to complete your code, then write out a short message to your sibling or mom or dad (you may want to use a scrap sheet of paper to practice your coded message). Give it to them to decipher.

A	B	C	D	E	F	G	H	I	J	K	L	M	N	O	P	Q	R	S	T	U	V	W	X	Y	Z
				12																					

```
___  ___   E       ___  ___  ___  ___  ___      ___  ___  ___   E   ___  ___
 10   14   12        8   26   19    6   14        8   25   22   12    9   23
```

```
Z  H  R  B  E  X  O  Q  B  R  D  I  S  V  Z
M  T  P  F  F  F  H  D  R  R  K  H  P  C  C
O  W  K  C  D  T  Z  S  F  A  Y  S  A  B  L
F  T  P  S  E  V  I  S  S  E  R  G  O  R  P
L  Q  G  A  N  O  I  N  U  B  A  E  R  R  N
U  L  N  J  K  B  S  P  S  Y  P  V  O  L  E
X  G  I  U  M  T  Q  W  T  D  H  N  D  P  W
X  W  S  H  R  M  U  U  L  D  R  X  V  B  Y
M  I  C  I  N  X  M  F  L  E  D  Z  W  I  O
G  P  K  J  Z  A  Y  I  V  T  O  L  E  R  R
Z  E  V  H  Q  J  U  O  C  A  T  E  C  A  K
N  C  A  I  S  M  G  J  I  H  K  U  M  S  E
T  O  Y  M  A  K  E  R  N  T  T  S  U  Y  S
N  S  I  M  W  B  Q  U  C  A  X  O  Q  N  I
J  A  C  S  E  U  I  J  M  O  S  M  M  B  C
```

Find the words: San Juan Hill, Governor, Union, Strike, Progressives, Teddy Bear, Michtom, New York, Toymaker

Note: Some words may appear backwards.

Across

3. Last name of airplane inventors
5. State of first airplane
6. Germany tried to send this to Mexico
7. U.S. President during World War I
8. The League of _____

Down

1. The Treaty of _____
2. British passenger ship
4. On April 6, congress declared war on _____.

The killings that happened on February 14 in Chicago became known as

_____.

OCALHOL

LALGILE

PASKE-SEAY

BETGOOGERL

MELGUGRS

GASGN

CEPNAO

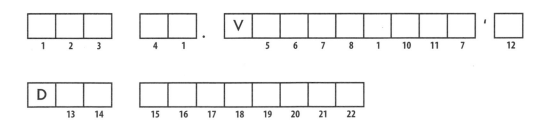

149

NEW YORK

WELCOME TO AMERICA

ELLIS

ISLAND

```
B   N   F   R   L   F   W   S   W   R   V   A   U   P   B
N   N   O   V   T   E   A   M   K   H   M   X   R   O   V
U   M   X   I   U   E   P   R   T   N   X   T   P   V   N
T   M   E   E   S   X   T   S   M   M   A   C   S   E   A
T   K   X   Y   H   S   E   I   W   E   C   B   Y   R   O
F   T   G   O   N   R   E   Q   G   Q   R   N   G   T   L
K   B   F   T   E   U   N   R   B   Y   N   S   N   Y   B
V   T   V   T   X   U   I   C   P   Q   N   P   I   X   N
E   E   N   A   Q   M   J   H   Y   E   H   T   H   G   Q
R   I   E   C   O   N   O   M   Y   U   D   I   S   O   W
X   X   A   C   Q   T   R   U   N   S   H   B   A   A   J
Y   R   T   T   G   T   U   G   X   C   J   O   R   X   L
Q   I   F   Y   E   T   E   G   G   Y   J   M   C   F   I
X   K   L   E   B   R   X   E   R   E   V   O   O   H   P
I   A   J   L   L   U   B   Q   L   J   V   D   W   L   R
```

Find the words: Depression, Banks, Crashing, Loan, Interest, Economy, Farmers, Hunger, Poverty, Hoover

Note: Some words may appear backwards.

Across

3. Place where weapons are made
5. Consists of forty-three soldiers
7. Said, "A day that will live in infamy."
8. The Japanese surrendered in a ceremony aboard the USS _____.

Down

1. The Battle of Iwo _____ was one of the fiercest fights in February of 1945.
2. Was bombed by Japanese
4. How Americans helped pay for the war
6. The _____ bomb destroyed two Japanese cities.

During the 1950s, this husband and wife were caught as spies when they provided top-secret information about radar and jet propulsion engines to the Russians.

BOBM RETLEHS

CLDO ARW

HERNEIWEOS

SISRSNAU

WIAHYHSG

ERD SAECR

SIEPS

CYRHAMCT

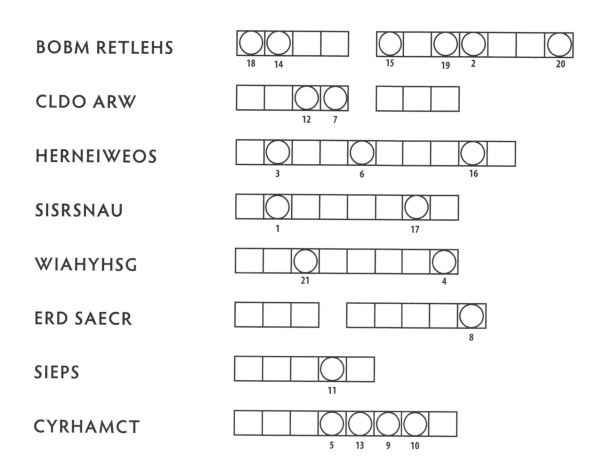

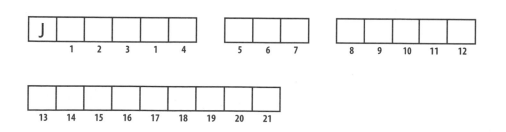

Fill in the blanks for the word search clues and then find the corresponding words in the word search.

1. Pledge of _____.

2. _____Fulton Sheen.

3. Life is worth _____.

4. Mass _____ was at an all-time high.

5. _____ to the priesthood and religious life were plentiful.

6. The top selling book was the _____.

7. The Knights of _____.

```
A  B  K  E  Q  F  H  R  V  S  X  P  T  E  A
R  L  D  S  T  M  K  G  D  L  J  C  M  E  H
C  R  L  A  U  R  Y  C  S  U  E  A  L  Z  P
H  S  B  E  O  B  J  H  X  O  T  B  A  Q  C
B  H  X  U  G  N  M  W  D  T  I  K  W  N  H
I  X  Q  K  E  I  W  U  E  B  B  N  C  N  F
S  Y  E  O  V  H  A  N  L  Y  G  V  G  K  V
H  J  W  A  A  G  D  N  L  O  C  T  G  B  O
O  L  A  L  G  A  T  G  C  Z  C  S  M  N  U
P  S  R  V  N  P  J  S  X  E  A  M  O  A  A
Q  T  O  C  I  G  L  W  V  Q  X  E  F  W  E
L  J  E  U  V  O  E  X  J  P  X  E  I  R  Z
J  Y  P  G  I  U  A  N  K  P  B  J  G  J  A
Y  K  K  U  L  A  C  Z  N  Y  K  W  N  C  Q
G  D  S  N  O  I  T  A  C  O  V  E  Z  U  G
```

Note: Some words may appear backwards.

After reading chapter 32, answer the following question.

In 1964, Congress outlawed all forms of discrimination based on race, gender, and nation of origin by passing the _____.

Once you have written in the correct answer, you should have a numeric symbol for most of the letters. Fill in a numeric symbol for the remaining letters of your own choosing (make sure to not repeat a number already used) to complete your code, then write out a short message to your sibling or mom or dad (you may want to use a scrap sheet of paper to practice your coded message). Give it to them to decipher.

A	B	C	D	E	F	G	H	I	J	K	L	M	N	O	P	Q	R	S	T	U	V	W	X	Y	Z

<u> </u> <u> </u> <u> </u>   <u> </u> <u> </u> <u> </u> <u> </u> <u> </u>   <u> </u> <u> </u> <u> </u> <u> </u> <u> </u> <u> </u>   <u> </u> <u> </u> <u> </u>

21 22 5   17 7 24 7 3   16 7 13 22 21 1   12 17 21

Across

3. Famous Civil Rights leader's last name
4. The Cuban _____ crisis
6. Became president after Kennedy

Down

1. Ku Klux _____
2. The Civil _____ Act
3. Assassinated in 1963 in Dallas
5. Russian satellite

Carter knew the nation had lots of problems, saying that the United States was suffering from a _____.

MECOYNO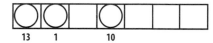
              13   1   10

LIO
          5

GAOSILNE
            7   11   14

HAGSOTRE
           9   2

DEIMDL SATE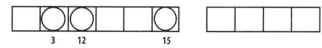
          3   12   15

MYJMI TEACRR
                 8

ELMASAI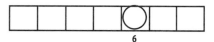
                4

BYEMASS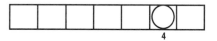
             6

| 1 | 2 | 3 | 4 | 5 | 6 | | 7 (F) | | 8 | 9 | 10 | (F) | 11 | 12 | 13 | 14 | 8 | 15 |

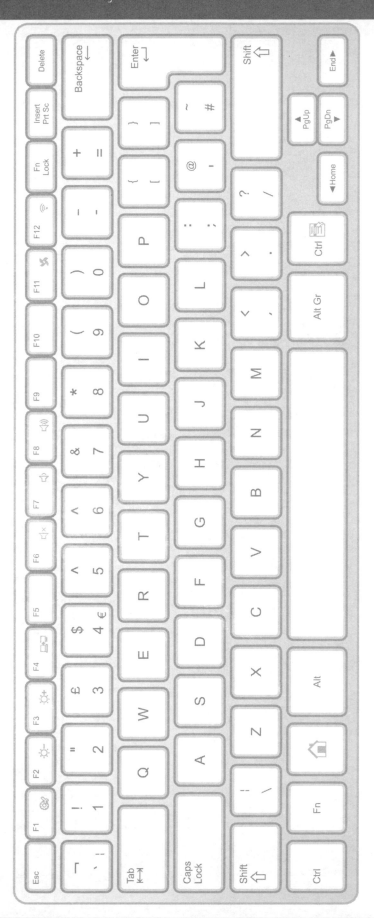

Across

2. The creator of the "WWW" was Tim Berners-_____.
5. Stands for electronic mail
6. President elected after George H. W. Bush
7. Short for inter-networking

Down

1. A downturn in the economy is called a _____.
3. When Congress attempts to forcibly remove a president from power.
4. "WWW" stands for _____ wide web.

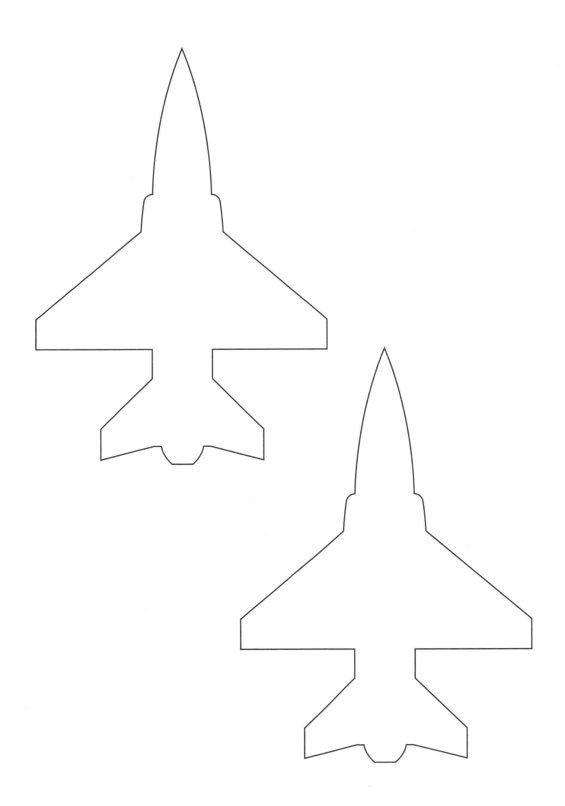

```
C O N S T I T U T I O N N Q C
B K T W B W N M T S C V E P X
Y I W R E L S O A F M P W C A
G A L B U I W C T P G S O F O
Q Z H L O M R Q N C A R R A W
U H W R O I P R R Y E J L D E
T V E R F F H N K B U J E D N
S H V I N M R C R L D H A P H
G F C E N R Z I I G K V N A E
V E O I E O H L G L E U S N K
S N A C I R E M A H O C M I G
O B A M A C Z E N G T H V R Y
M T G B D H P S M F V S T T U
Z Y J L W E G G C S K S E A K
P N R J X R L I E L R N F K C
```

Find the words: Katrina, New Orleans, Obama, Trump, Heroism, Sacrifice, Catholic, Americans, Constitution, Bill of Rights

Note: Some words may appear backwards.

After reading the last chapter in the text, answer the following question.

Who said inspiring words to Americans in Denver, CO on World Youth Day in 1993?

Once you have written in the correct answer, you should have a numeric symbol for most of the letters. Fill in a numeric symbol for the remaining letters of your own choosing (make sure to not repeat a number already used) to complete your code, then write out a short message to your sibling or mom or dad (you may want to use a scrap sheet of paper to practice your coded message). Give it to them to decipher.

A	B	C	D	E	F	G	H	I	J	K	L	M	N	O	P	Q	R	S	T	U	V	W	X	Y	Z
															4										

$$\underset{4}{P}\ \underset{7}{\_}\ \underset{4}{P}\ \underset{12}{\_}\quad \underset{1}{\_}\ \underset{22}{\_}\ \cdot\ \underset{23}{\_}\ \underset{7}{\_}\ \underset{17}{\_}\ \underset{14}{\_}\quad \underset{4}{P}\ \underset{11}{\_}\ \underset{10}{\_}\ \underset{9}{\_}\quad \underset{8}{\_}\ \underset{8}{\_}$$